The King's hole
and other stories

M
Macmillan Education

C000094941

The King's hole

The King found a hole in a field.
It was round and deep and
he couldn't see the bottom.
Is there anyone in there? he called.
Come out if there is, he shouted.
But no one called out and
no one came out.
I shall keep this hole for myself,
said the King.

I must put something in the hole,
said the King.
He looked down the hole again.
I know what I'll do, he said.
I'll put a rabbit down the hole.
So he went round the field
to look for a rabbit.

He saw a big brown rabbit in
the long grass.
The King picked him up and
put him down the hole.
Now the King had a big brown rabbit
in his big brown hole.
The King looked down the hole but
he couldn't see the rabbit at all.
Come out, he shouted.

But the big brown rabbit didn't want
to come out of the hole.
Oh bother, said the King and
he stamped his foot.
Come out, he shouted again.
The rabbit came out of the hole and
ran away.

Now what shall I put in my hole?
said the King.
I know, I'll put a big fat worm in it.
So the King got a big fat worm and
put it in the hole.
The King looked down his hole but
he couldn't see the worm at all.
Come out, he shouted but
the worm didn't want to come out.

The King was very cross.
Oh bother, he said and
he stamped his foot.
Some soil on the edge fell
into the hole and the King
stamped his foot again.
Lots more soil fell into
the hole and the wind blew
some seeds across the field.

The King was so cross that he went home.
He didn't go to the hole for a long time.
Then one day he said,
I will go and look at my hole.
Perhaps I can think of something
to put in it after all.
So the King went to look at the hole.
But he couldn't find his hole
in the field.

He found lots of little yellow flowers
but there was no hole at all.
I wonder where all those flowers
came from, said the King.
I like them better than my hole and
they won't run away.

How the tortoise got his shell

A long time ago the gods lived
high up in the sky.
One day they wanted to have a party.
We will ask all the animals on earth
to our party, they said.

But only the birds could
go to the party.
All the other animals could not fly
high up into the sky.
They had to stay at home.
Tortoise was sad.
He wanted to go to the party.
Then he had an idea.
Stop! he shouted to the birds.
Don't go without me!

You can't come with us, said the birds.
You have no wings. How will you fly?
I can fly if you will help me,
said the tortoise.
Give me a feather from your wings.
So all the birds gave the tortoise
a feather and the tortoise made
a fine pair of wings.
He stuck the wings on his shell.

Now I can fly, said the tortoise.
Now I can go to the party.
But now that I have wings
I need a new name.
My wings are made from feathers from
all of you.
So my new name shall be All-of-You.
What a good name, said the birds.
Then they all went off to the party.

There was lots of food at the party.
Tortoise was very hungry.
He wanted all the food for himself.
Who is all the food for? he asked.
It's for all of you, said the gods.
They did not know that
the tortoise had a new name.
Oh good, said the tortoise.
It's all for me, and he ate it all up.
The birds didn't have any food at all.

The birds were very cross so
they took back all their feathers.
Now you will have to get home
by yourself, they said.
Then they left the tortoise in the sky.
The tortoise called down to his wife.
I am going to jump down from the sky,
he said.
Get some leaves and grass for me
to land on.

But the birds were still cross so
they took the leaves and grass away.
The tortoise jumped and
landed on the ground with a **bang**.
His shell broke into lots of little bits.
His wife stuck them all together again
very carefully.
But if you look at a tortoise,
you will see where the tortoise broke
his shell and where his wife stuck all
the bits together again.

Gone is gone

Peter lived on a farm with his wife Lisa and
their baby girl Katy.
They had a dog called Spot, one cow,
two goats, three pigs and ten hens.
Peter worked hard in the fields.
Lisa worked hard in the house and
she looked after the baby.
But every day Peter said to Lisa,
You do not work as hard as I do.
Your work in the house is easy.

One day Lisa said to him,
If you think my work is so easy,
today you do my work and
I will do yours.
Now don't forget to take the cow to
the field, make the soup and
clean the house.
Look after the baby and
don't let Spot into the kitchen.

Lisa went to work in the fields and
Peter sat in the sun.
This will be an easy day for me,
he said. There's lots of time.
After a while he went inside.
I'm hungry, he said.
I will cook some sausages to eat.
So he put some sausages in the pan.

I am so hot, he said. I will get
a mug of beer from the barrel.
He went to the barrel and
began to pour out the beer.
Then he heard a noise in the kitchen.
Oh dear, he said. I have left the door
open and Spot has come into the kitchen.
He rushed up to the kitchen and
what did he see?
Spot was running away with
the sausages.

Never mind, he said.
What's gone is gone.
He went back to the barrel but
he had left the tap on and
there was beer all over the floor.
I will wipe it up later, he said.
Now I must see to the cow.
It is too far to take her to the field.
There is lots of grass on the roof.
She can eat that.

So Peter took the cow up on the roof.
He tied a long piece of rope to her leg and
put the other end down the chimney.
That will stop her running away, he said.
Then he went back into the house and
tied the other end of the rope
round his middle.
Now I must make the soup, he said.
He put the big soup pot on the fire but
Oh dear, just then there was
a bump and a thud.

The cow had fallen off the roof.
That gave a big tug to the rope and
Peter was pulled half way
up the chimney.
When Lisa came home, she saw the cow
hanging from the roof so
she cut the rope.

Down came the cow, but inside the house
down came Peter and he landed with
a splash right inside the soup pot.
When Lisa helped him out he said,
Oh Lisa, I'll do my work and
you do yours.
Never again will I say that
your work is easy.
And from that day to this,
they lived happily ever after.